Show the pattern using different c

I can find more than one way!

What comes next?

What comes next?

ELG 12: Mathematics: Shape, space and measures explore characteristics of everyday objects and shapes and use mathematical language to describe them recognise, create and describe patterns

Strengthen: *Can you point to each picture and describe each object? Can you circle each part that repeats? How could you show what comes next?*

Deepen: *How do you know it is a pattern? Could you continue the pattern even further? What is the same and what is different about the patterns on the page?*

4

What comes next?

Complete the pattern.

ELG 12: Mathematics: Shape, space and measures explore characteristics of everyday objects and shapes and use mathematical language to describe them
recognise, create and describe patterns

Strengthen: *Can you point to each picture and use words to describe each item in the row? Can you circle each part that repeats? What do you think comes next? How can you show this on the page?*
Deepen: *How do you know this is a pattern? Can you continue the pattern even further? What is the same and what is different about the patterns on the page? Can you continue the pattern in the other direction?*

Power Maths

Reception
Maths Journal
C

My name is _____.

I am in_____.

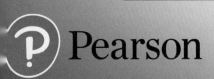

Show the pattern in a different way.

I will use [cube] and [cube].

 Strengthen: *What pattern can you see? What is the repeating part of the pattern? Can you circle the part that repeats? Can you say the pattern out loud? What two different objects would you like to use to copy the pattern?* [Give suggestions such as 3D shapes or buttons, or refer children to what Dexter is saying about using cubes.]

Deepen: *How many different ways could you show this pattern? Can you give each item in the pattern a name, such as an A or a B? How could you describe this pattern? Is it an AB pattern? An ABB pattern? An AAB pattern? Can you make this pattern with actions, with sounds and with objects? What is the same about the patterns? What is different about the patterns?*

Circle the number the counter will land on.

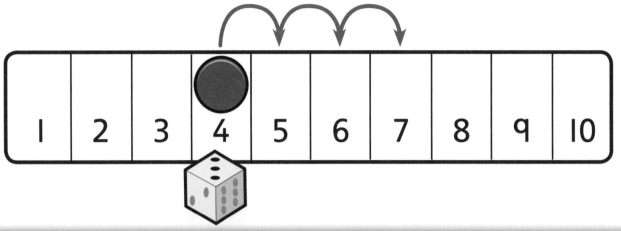

Circle the number the counter will land on.

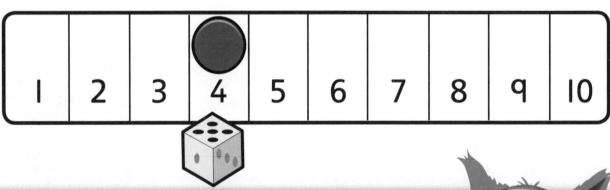

Use your finger to help you count the jumps.

ELG 11: Mathematics: Numbers count reliably with numbers from 1 to 10 using quantities and objects, add and subtract 2 single-digit numbers and count on to find the answer

Ask **Strengthen:** *Where is the counter? What number is on the dice? How many jumps will the counter make? Do you count the number the counter is on? Where will the counter land? Can you use a real counter to help you? Can you use your finger to count the jumps?*
Deepen: *What is the same about both number tracks? How do you know when to stop counting on? Can you use your finger to check you have counted correctly?*

First there were 4 children playing.
Then ___ children joined in.
Now there are ___ children playing.

| 1 | 2 | 3 | 4 | 5 | 6 | 7 | 8 | 9 | 10 |

Ask

Strengthen: *How many children are playing at first? How can you show that? How many children are not playing? Could one child join in? How would you show this? What number would you count on from? How many will you count on? How many are there now? Can more than one child join in? What if ___ children joined in? How would the story change?*
Deepen: *How many different ways can you complete the story? What is the smallest/biggest number of children that can be playing? How? Can you describe it using a first, then, now story? Can you work systematically? Can you explain your system?*

Go back 5.

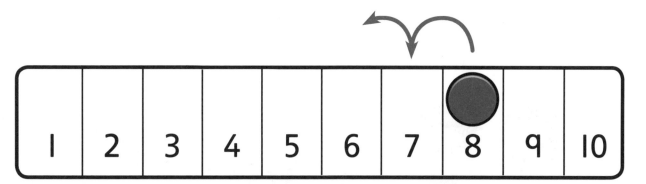

Go back 6.

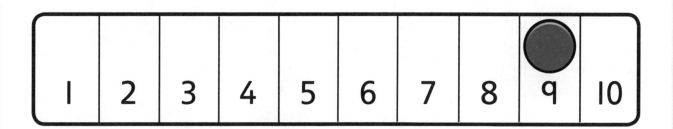

ELG 11: Mathematics: Numbers count reliably with numbers from 1 to 10 using quantities and objects, add and subtract 2 single-digit numbers and count on or back to find the answer

Strengthen: *In which direction do you need to move? How many squares back do you need to move? How can you keep track of how many you have counted back? What number comes before 8?*

Deepen: *How do you know where to count back from? What if the counter had been on ___? Where would you have started counting from? Where would you have ended up? How did you know when to stop counting? What is the biggest number you could have counted back? How do you know? Why couldn't you have counted back 9?*

Where might Hana land?

| 1 | 2 | 3 | 4 | 5 | 6 | 7 | 8 | 9 | 10 |

I will try all the numbers!

 Strengthen: *What number is Hana starting on? How do you know? What if the card says 'Go back 1'? How many would you need to count back? What number would Hana land on? What else could the card say? Could you count back that many? What number would Hana land on? Encourage children to work systematically, counting back 2, 3, 4, 5 and so on.*
Deepen: *Can you find all the possible answers? How do you know you have found them all? What is the smallest number that could be on the card? How do you know? How many would you need to count back? Can you describe it using a first, then, now story? What is the biggest number that you could count back? How do you know? Give children problems such as: I count back 4. I am now on 5. Where did I start? Explain how you know.*

What is one less than 13?

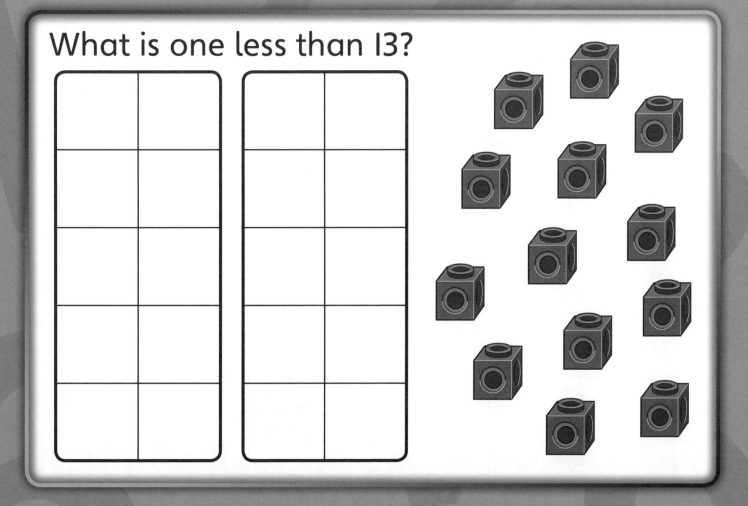

One more than 19 is ___.

ELG 11: Mathematics: Numbers count reliably with numbers from 1 to 20 and say which number is one more or one less than a given number

 Strengthen: *How many cubes are there? How could you use real cubes and the ten frames to help you? How can you show one less/one more? Will your amount get bigger or smaller? Why? Do you need to count forwards or backwards? Can you use a number track to count backwards to find the answer?*

Deepen: *How many full ten frames will you have? How do you know? How many cubes will be on the second ten frame? Once you have taken one away/added one, do you need to count all of the cubes again? Why not? What would one less/one more than your answer be? How do you know?*

Show 12.

1	2	3	4	5	6	7	8	9	10	11	12	13	14	15	16	17	18	19	20

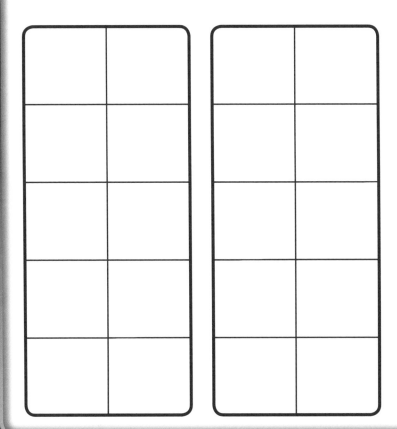

How many different ways can I show 12?

Ask **Strengthen:** *What could you use/draw to show 12? Where are you going to start counting from? Where are you going to stop counting? What number comes after 11 (or 9 or 6)? How many have you got now? Is there another way you could show 12? How would you use two ten frames to show 12?*

Deepen: *Can you explain what you have shown? What does each object represent? Is there a different way to show 12? [Show an incorrect representation.] Is this correct? Why not? How many more or fewer are needed? How many ways can you find?*

Draw spots to show the double.

Double 4 is ___ .

Draw spots to show a double.

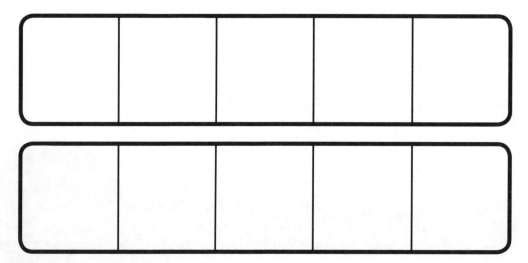

Double ___ is ___ .

ELG 11: Mathematics: Numbers solve problems, including doubling
ELG 12: Mathematics: Shape, space and measures recognise, create and describe patterns

Strengthen: *How many dots are on the domino already? Does the other side need to show the same or a different amount to make a double? What would double ___ look like? How many spots will you draw? How many spots are there altogether? What double could you show on the five frames? How many do you need to draw in the second five frame?*
Deepen: *How can you work out double 4? How many altogether? Can you say 'Double ___ is ___.'? How many different doubles can you make with five frames? What is the largest double you can make? What is the smallest double you can make?*

How many doubles can you show?

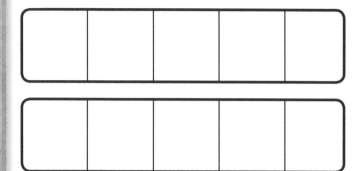 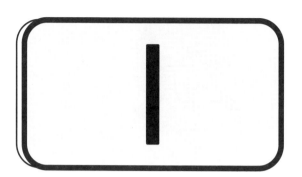

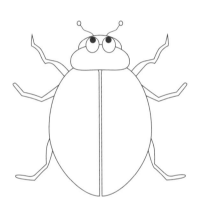

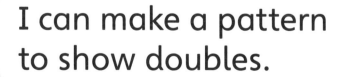

I can make a pattern to show doubles.

Share the .

Find half of the 🍒.

Half of 6 is ___.

ELG 11: Mathematics: Numbers solve problems, including doubling, halving and sharing

 Strengthen: *How many sandwiches are there altogether? What could you use to represent them? How can you share them? Have you shared them fairly? Do both children have the same? How can you find half of the cherries? What can you use instead of cherries? Can you use sharing to help you find half? Have you shared the cherries into two equal groups? How many are there in each equal part? What is half of 6?*

Deepen: *Can you predict the answer to half of 6? How did you work it out? How do you know you are right? What if there were 8 cherries? What is half of 8? How do you know? If double 2 is 4, what is half of 4? If half of 6 is 3, what is double 3? How can you use double 5 equals 10 to work out half of 10?*

Write half of each number. Use ⬭ on ▭▭▭▭.

Half of 2 is ___.

Half of 4 is ___.

Half of 6 is ___.

Half of 8 is ___.

I can see what will come next!

 Strengthen: *What does finding half mean? How can you find half? Can you share the counters into the five frames? Are the groups equal? How do you know?*
Can you say the sentence 'Half of ____ is ____.'? Can you see a pattern?
Deepen: *How will you find half? Do you need to share the counters between the five frames or can you see another way to work it out? How can you check you are right? Can you see a pattern? What do you think the next half will be? Can you say all the halving facts and the matching double facts? Can you find half of any other numbers?*

Can you share the ◯ into 2 equal groups?

odd   even

8 is an _____ number.

Can you share the ⬭ into equal groups?

_____ is an _____ number.

ELG 11: Mathematics: Numbers solve problems, including doubling, halving and sharing

 Strengthen: *What could you use to represent the balls? Can you use a counter for each ball? How could you find out if they will go into equal groups? How many counters have you put on each five frame? Are the groups equal? Is the number odd or even?*
Deepen: *How do you know if each number is odd or even? Could you use the five frames to show some different odd numbers? Could you show some even numbers? Can you make an odd number less than 5?*

Show an even number.

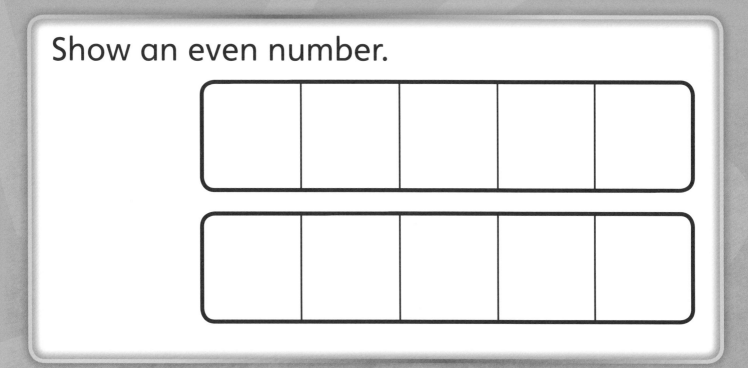

Show an odd number.

 Strengthen: *How do you know if a number is even? How do you know if a number is odd? Choose a number to try first. Use counters to show your number. Can you share the counters into two equal groups? Does that mean it is odd or even?*

Deepen: *Can you predict whether your number is odd or even? How can you check? What will be the next even number? What is the one before it? Can you find all the even numbers to 10? Is there a pattern? What are the odd numbers to 10? Explain how you know that (5) is odd/(6) is even.*

Which crayon is shorter?

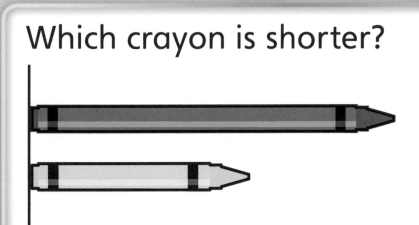

Which is taller?

ELG 12: Mathematics: Shape, space and measures use everyday language to talk about size to compare objects
explore characteristics of everyday objects and use mathematical language to describe them
ELG 4: Physical development: Moving and handling show good control and co-ordination in large and small movements
handle equipment and tools effectively, including pencils for writing

Ask

Strengthen: *Which crayon looks shorter? Which crayon is longer? How can you check which crayon is shorter? Which giraffe is taller? Which giraffe is shorter? How can you check? Can you find something that is shorter than the yellow crayon? Can you find something that is longer than the red crayon? Are you taller or shorter than a real giraffe?*

Deepen: *How can you check using multilink cubes which crayon is shorter? How can you check which giraffe is taller? Can you draw a crayon that is longer than the red crayon? Can you draw a crayon that is shorter than the yellow crayon? Can you find or draw something that is longer than the yellow crayon but shorter than the red crayon? How many cubes long would it have to be?*

Draw something longer than the .

I will line up objects with the end of the pencil.

Strengthen: Give children three or four items to choose from, some longer and some shorter than the pencil. Encourage them to measure the objects against the picture. *Which one is longer? Which one is shorter? Where should you put the object to see whether it is longer or shorter?* [Align to the baseline.] *Is your object shorter or longer than this one?*

Deepen: *How can you check that what you have drawn is longer? Do you need to draw a baseline? Can you draw something shorter? How many things can you find in the classroom that are shorter/longer than the pencil? Can you find three objects and put them in order, shortest to longest?*

Which is heavier?

The _____ is heavier than the _____.

block   teddy

The ☐ is _____ than the 🚗.

heavier   lighter

ELG 12: Mathematics: Shape, space and measures use everyday language to talk about weight to compare objects and to solve problems

explore characteristics of everyday objects and use mathematical language to describe them

ELG 4: Physical development: Moving and handling show good control and co-ordination in large and small movements

handle equipment and tools effectively, including pencils for writing

 Strengthen: *Look at the objects on the balance scales. What do you notice? Which object is heavier? Which object is lighter? How do you know? Can you find an object that is heavier than ____? Can you find an object that is lighter than ____?*

Deepen: *How do balance scales show which item is heavier? Which direction does the item go on the balance scales if it is heavier/lighter? What happens on the balance scales if the items weigh the same? Look at both of the balance scales. If the block is heavier than the teddy but lighter than the car, which is heavier, the teddy or the car? Which is the lightest – the car, the teddy or the block? Can you order the items, heaviest to lightest?*

Draw something lighter than the .

The _____ is lighter than the ☐ .

Draw something heavier than the ☐ .

The _____ is heavier than the ☐ .

 Strengthen: *Can you find an item that is lighter than a block? Where would you draw that on the picture? How do you know it is lighter? Can you find a heavier item? How do you know it is heavier? Where would it go on the picture?*
Deepen: *How many different items can you find? Can you order your items from lightest to heaviest? How could you use cubes on the scales to check which item is heavier/lighter/ heaviest/lightest?*

Colour in the bucket to show that it is full.

Colour in the bucket to show that it is nearly empty.

ELG 12: Mathematics: Shape, space and measures use everyday language to talk about capacity to compare quantities
explore characteristics of everyday objects and use mathematical language to describe them
ELG 4: Physical development: Moving and handling show good control and co-ordination in large and small movements
handle equipment and tools effectively, including pencils for writing

Ask

Strengthen: *What does full mean? How can you show that this bucket is full? Would you be able to fit any more in? What does empty mean? What does nearly empty mean? How can you show that this bucket is nearly empty?*
Deepen: *What could you use to fill a bucket? How much of the bucket do you need to colour to show that it is full? How much of the bucket do you need to colour to show that it is nearly empty? Is there more than one way to show this? Is there more than one way to show nearly empty? What would a bucket that is nearly full look like? Is there more than one way to show this? If a bucket is nearly empty, can you fill it some more? If a bucket is nearly full, can you fit more in?*

Show a cup that has more sand.
Show a cup that has less sand.

more   less

I think there is more
than one way to do this.

Strengthen: *Can you show a cup with the same amount of sand as the picture? How could you show a cup that has more sand than this? Can you show a cup with less sand? Would a full cup have more or less sand than the cup in the middle? Would an empty cup have more or less sand than the cup in the middle?*

Deepen: *Do all the cups need to be the same size? How could you be sure a cup has more sand in it? [Make it full.] How could you be sure a cup has less sand in it? [Make it empty.] Would a nearly full cup have more or less sand than the cup in the middle? Would a nearly empty cup have more or less sand than the cup in the middle?*

Power Maths

Reception
Maths Journal C

How to use this book

We recommend that children have adult support to use this book. Children who are not yet confident with mark-making can demonstrate their mathematical understanding by placing real-life objects, such as cubes, on the page.

Practice pages encourage children to practise the new skills they have learned in their Power Maths lessons.

Reflect gives children an opportunity to demonstrate their depth of understanding at the end of each week.

At the bottom of each page you will find prompt questions for the adult helper.

Strengthen questions support children who are not sure where to start.

Deepen questions encourage children to develop a deeper understanding of the concept.

Dexter   **Astrid**   **Sparks**

Published by Pearson Education Limited, 80 Strand, London, WC2R 0RL.

www.pearsonschools.co.uk

Text and design © Pearson Education Limited 2019

Edited by Pearson and Just Content Ltd

Design templates created by Kamae Design

Typeset by PDQ Media

Original illustrations © Pearson Education Limited 2019

Illustrated by Andrew Painter and Nadene Naude at Beehive Illustration

Cover design by Pearson Education Ltd
Cover illustration by Andrew Painter
Back cover illustration by Andrew Painter

Power Maths Series Editor and Power Maths Reception Consultant: Tony Staneff

Written by White Rose Maths (Beth Smith, Amy How, Jane Brown and Faye Hirst), Beth Smith, Katie Williams, Faye Hirst and Caroline Hamilton.

First published 2019

23 22 21 20 19

10 9 8 7 6 5 4 3 2 1

British Library Cataloguing in Publication Data

A catalogue record for this book is available from the British Library

ISBN 978 1 292 28609 9

Printed in the UK by Ashford Press Ltd

www.activelearnprimary.co.uk

Note from the publisher

Pearson has robust editorial processes, including answer and fact checks, to ensure the accuracy of the content in this publication, and every effort is made to ensure this publication is free of errors. We are, however, only human, and occasionally errors do occur. Pearson is not liable for any misunderstandings that arise as a result of errors in this publication, but it is our priority to ensure that the content is accurate. If you spot an error, please do contact us at resourcescorrections@pearson.com so we can make sure it is corrected.

www.pearsonschools.co.uk
myorders@pearson.com

ISBN 978-1-292-28609-9

Pearson